CW00846988

Infinite Space

Story by **Christian Grenier**
Factual accounts
and activities by **Guillaume Cannat**

contents

Story

Mega-infos

Activity

Mega-infos

Anecdotes

Mega-infos

Activity

Mega-infos

Game

Mega-infos

Quiz

Stickers

Picture Cards

Story

The Pilgrim of the Stars

Christian Grenier

Lost in Space

"This is very important, Kiri-2. I repeat: Why did the *Sagan II,* our spaceship, break down?" His throat tight, Allan waited, watching the screen. Two seconds later, the computer answered him in a pleasant voice:

"I am upset, Allan. An accident

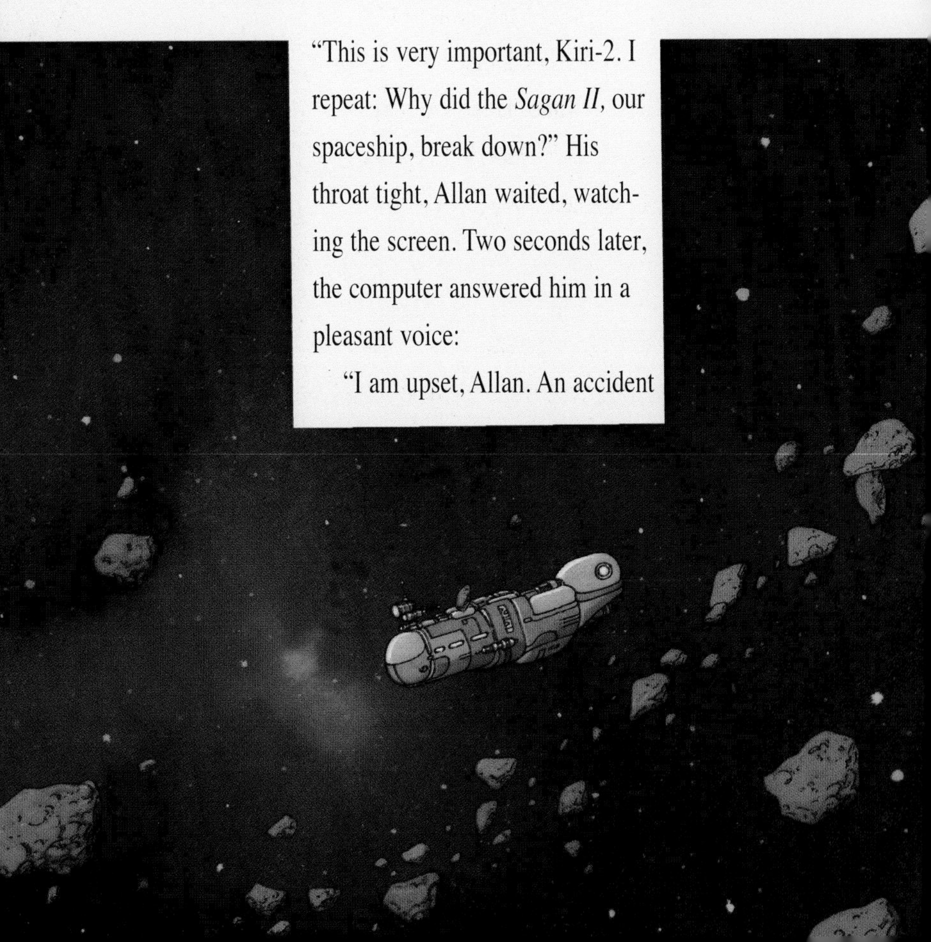

has destroyed my circuits. I cannot answer your question. Ask Kiri, the main computer."

"If I am asking you, it is because Kiri is out of order! You, a backup computer? You must be kidding!"

"I am upset, Allan. An accident has destroyed my..."

Annoyed, Allan unplugged Kiri-2. He looked up toward the porthole where he could see thousands of stars and sighed. "Okay. So, we are condemned to wander in the cosmos until the end of time. This spaceship will be our tomb." He slumped in his chair, holding his head between his hands and groaned. "Why...why did we leave?"

It was simple: Allan and his friend Lynn were attracted by adventure. On Earth, thanks to the new Hubble 4 space telescope, a planet capable of supporting life was detected around Altair. Ten volunteers were recruited. Their mission? To populate another solar system. Allan even hoped that they would be the first to discover a form of intelligent life. Not too long ago, radio telescopes had received organized messages—proof the universe was inhabited!

Alas, no contact had yet been made. Even though it only housed twelve passengers, the spaceship *Sagan II*

was as large as a city. It had left Earth fifteen years earlier to reach Altair. Its fabulous speed was close to that of the speed of light: 186,282 miles (299,792 km) per second. In spite of that, the trip would last seventeen years!

That is why the trip was being made in hibernation. Each astronaut slept eleven months of each year and was responsible for supervising the ship the remaining month. But shortly before, Kiri had given the alert:

"Allan? The *Sagan II* has deviated from its course. You must make a manual course correction."

"What? You are programmed for that sort of thing, aren't you?"

"Yes. But the controls for the auxiliary motors are no longer responding. My circuits are burned out, I cannot make the repair."

"What...what did you say?"

For some unknown reason, the controls of the *Sagan II* had been damaged and the two computers put out of service; without their help, any repair was impossible! On board a ship that was traveling blind, the humans had become bits of dust lost in the ocean of the cosmos.

"I must wake up Lynn and the others. I must tell them the truth." Arriving near the hibernation compartments, Allan hesitated: wouldn't it be better to let his companions sleep?

At that moment, a strident ringing was heard. Alan thought that his heart would fail him. What new catastrophe had arrived? Running, he returned to the command room. When he made out the signals on the screens, he couldn't believe his eyes: Radar had detected an enormous object in space that was approaching their spaceship.

"I'm dreaming...this isn't possible. We are the only Earthlings in this area of the Galaxy. It must be..."

Soon, a ship drew alongside the *Sagan II*. Its fuselage glowed with a blue light. A luminous being left the strange vessel and began to float through space. Incredulous, Allan wondered how he should act. He observed without understanding the unknown being outside who seemed to be signaling him.

"Of course. He wants me to open the airlock!" Allan executed the maneuver. The creature that entered the command room had the shape of a human and wore a sparkling suit. A smile lit up his peaceful face.

Coming from nowhere, a voice surged in Allan's head: "Welcome, voyager. Can I be of some assistance? Express yourself by thinking; I do not speak your language."

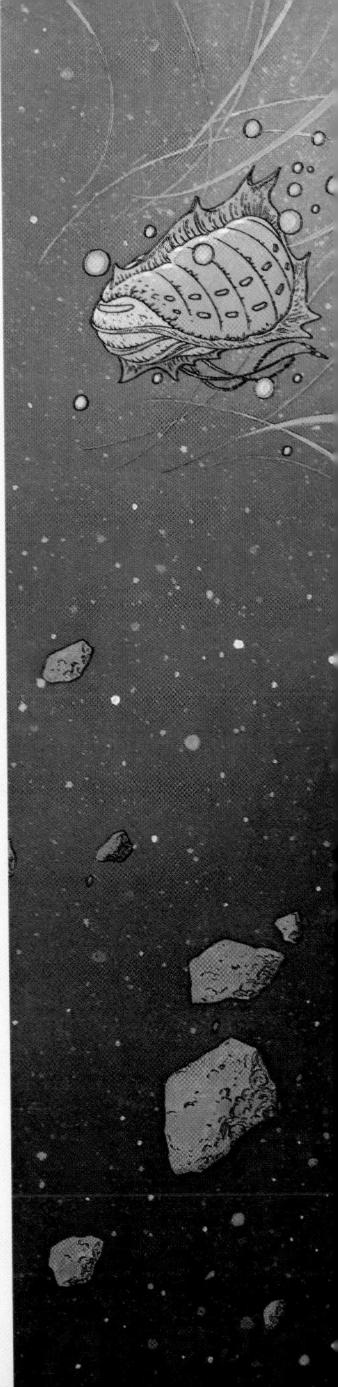

Story

Moved, stupefied, Allan stammered to himself: "But...who are you? Where do you come from? And why did you stop?"

"My name is O-O-T. I am a pilgrim. I come from a faraway galaxy. Our paths crossed, I am afraid...Will you allow me?" With his index finger, O-O-T brushed the command screen. A gleam seemed to pass through the body of the extraterrestrial. "Yes, the radiation from my engine has damaged your computers and altered your ship's controls. Rest assured, I am in the process of repairing these damages..."

Allan understood that O-O-T was using remote control. In this way, they reached the Altair solar system! Thinking about Lynn and their future together, he felt a rush of happiness.

"Altair? Superb star. This system has ten planets. Two are inhabited. A third is uninhabited but capable of supporting life. It has an ocean and a continent."

"So, do you come from Altair?"

"Me? Oh, no! From much further. I left ten billion years ago."

Allan thought he had misunderstood. But in the cosmos, constants do exist, such as the speed of light. And the numbers provided by O-O-T left no doubt.

An Almost Immortal Traveler

"I was born three billion years after the big bang."

"But...how long do you think you still have to live?"

"I am afraid that the life span of Earthlings is short," said the extraterrestrial pointing to the hibernation cases. "Me, I hope to travel through more galaxies, to brush past blue giants and white dwarfs, to get close to comets and to black holes, to be present for the explosions of supernovae."

Allan remembered that, on Earth, some insects live only for a season—sometimes even only for a few days. Compared with O-O-T, he felt terribly fragile. Yet this extraterrestrial looked very much like a human!

"You are mistaken: I only adopted this form to better communicate with you. My appearance is not important! There...the repairs are done."

Already, the luminous being was moving away. Allan cried out, "Wait, O-O-T! I know nothing about you! Will we see each other again?"

"No, I must continue on my pilgrimage. Life is so short—"

"What is your objective? Where are you going? When will you return home?"

These questions seemed to embarrass O-O-T—as if a human being was not capable of understanding the answers.

"My objective is knowledge. When you look at a universe that does not cease to grow and to expand, science is a voyage without return, Allan...Oh, I'm sorry, my energy must have burned your chair. The fabric is scorched." The pilgrim drew away from Allan.

"Good-bye. I wish you and Lynn a happy life!"

When the strange spaceship had disappeared into space, Allan asked himself for a long time whether he had been dreaming. He awakened Lynn and the others and told them about the incredible meeting.

"Of course, you were dreaming!" exclaimed Lynn, laughing. "Such pure energy doesn't exist. Look: the computers are working."

"Yes. And the controls are in perfect condition."

"But what have you done to your chair? It is burned to a crisp!"

"His name was O-O-T," repeated Allan, stubbornly. "He was a pilgrim of the stars from a faraway galaxy. Look at what he told me about Altair..."

When the *Sagan II* arrived in view of the star, the two computers on board delivered a mass of data: "Radar is detecting ten planets..."

"Two appear to be already inhabited!" exclaimed Lynn. "The third is capable of supporting life."

"Yes," murmured Allan. "It is covered with an ocean and a single continent. That is where we are going to land and where we are going to settle."

Impressed, the others agreed. And when the *Sagan II* turned its course toward this uninhabited, hospitable world, Allan took Lynn's hand and smiled. He was thinking that one day, in the distant future, the children of their children would perhaps cross the path of O-O-T, the mysterious pilgrim of the stars.

The Imagined Universe

From the time of the caveman to modern times, each civilization has attempted to explain the existence and the movement of the stars that populate the sky.

The Crystal Spheres of the Greeks

Almost 2,500 years ago, Greek thinkers imagined that the Sun, the Moon, the planets, and all the other stars were positioned on crystal spheres that revolved around Earth. They also affirmed that the movement of these spheres produced a harmonious music called “the music of the spheres.”

In 1609, Galileo was the first to observe the sky with a telescope.

❦ ***Maya***
Central American people whose civilization peaked one thousand years ago.

The Universe of the Maya

For the **Maya,**❦ the world was balanced on the shell of an enormous tortoise that swam in an infinite ocean. The movements of the tortoise caused earthquakes. The stars were little flames attached to a dome held up by four giant trees.

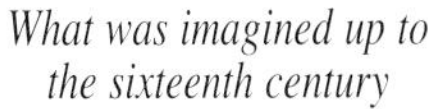
What was imagined up to the sixteenth century

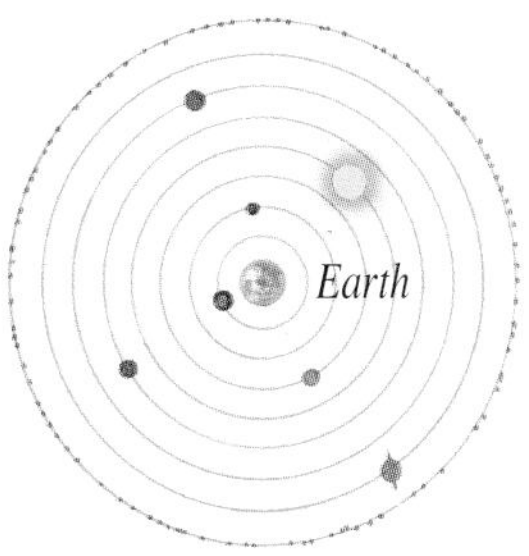

A Closed World

Until well into the Renaissance, Arab and European scientists thought that the universe ended at crystal spheres. For them, Earth was the center of the universe. The Sun, the Moon, the planets, and the stars revolved around it. This is called a geocentric universe.

What we believe today

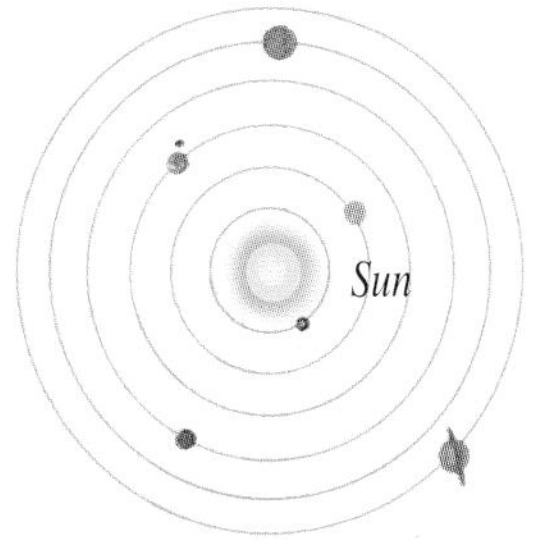

❦ ***Heliocentrism***
*The Sun (*helios *in Greek) is at the center of the solar system and the planets, like the Earth, revolve around it.*

The Invention of the Modern Universe

In 1543, Nicolas Copernicus affirmed that the Sun, not Earth, is the center of the universe, contrary to that which was written in the Bible. His **heliocentric** ❦ theory took decades to become accepted. In fact, it was necessary to wait until the beginning of the seventeenth century, and the observations of the Italian Galileo with his telescope, to prove that Copernicus was right.

The Known Universe

❦ *Galaxy*
This word comes from the Greek gala xia *meaning "path of milk" or "milky way."*

Today, astronomers consider the universe infinite, populated by billions of galaxies.❦

The Age of the Universe

Astronomers have a difficult time agreeing on the age of the universe. For some, it is 20 billion years old, while others say it is "only" 10 billion years old. Whatever its age, the universe is old enough for there to have been several generations of stars. Our Sun is only 4.5 billion years old.

Matter cooling after the big bang.

big bang

galaxies

Bits of gas of which galaxies are formed.

Perpetual and Rapid Expansion?

In the 1920s, the astronomers Vesto Melvin Slipher and Edwin Hubble showed that the galaxies were separating from each other, with the more distant ones moving away faster than the nearer ones. This is similar to the behavior of raisins during the baking of a cake. The cake rises and, on the inside, the raisins follow the movement by separating from each other.

Billions of Galaxies

In certain photographs of the sky made by the world's most powerful telescopes, taken either from Earth or in space, tens of thousands of galaxies can be counted. That means that in the whole of space, the existence of more than 50 billion galaxies can be imagined.

The Galaxies

A single galaxy can contain several hundreds of billions of stars. There are several types of galaxies.

The giant Andromeda galaxy is a spiral galaxy.

Families of Stars

Take two hundred billion stars, some gas, some dust, and lots of empty space. Mix them all together to give the shape of a pancake, slightly thicker in the center than at the edges, and you will get our galaxy, commonly known as the Milky Way.

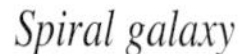

Spiral galaxy

Two Spirals of Fireworks

Galaxies revolve around their centers for several hundreds of millions of years. This rotation gives them the appearance of large pinwheels. You can easily recreate the form of galaxies by stirring tea in a cup. If the tea is properly steeped and there is some foam, you will see this foam form a spiral in the center of the cup.

A Mixture of Galaxies

Some years ago, astronomers who wished to know what the universe looks like decided to construct a model. They used a powerful computer to calculate the positions of several million galaxies "close" to ours. Surprise! If, on a small scale, the galaxies are collected in packets, on a large scale, they seem to be distributed throughout the universe like bits of dust on the surface of enormous empty bubbles.

Quasars

Known for the last 30 years, **quasars** nevertheless remain mysterious. They are incredibly bright and distant. According to the latest theories, the huge amount of energy emitted by quasars is supplied by large "black holes" at their centers.

Quasar
Contraction of the expression "quasi-stellar," which literally means half-starlike.

Barred spiral galaxy

Elliptical galaxy

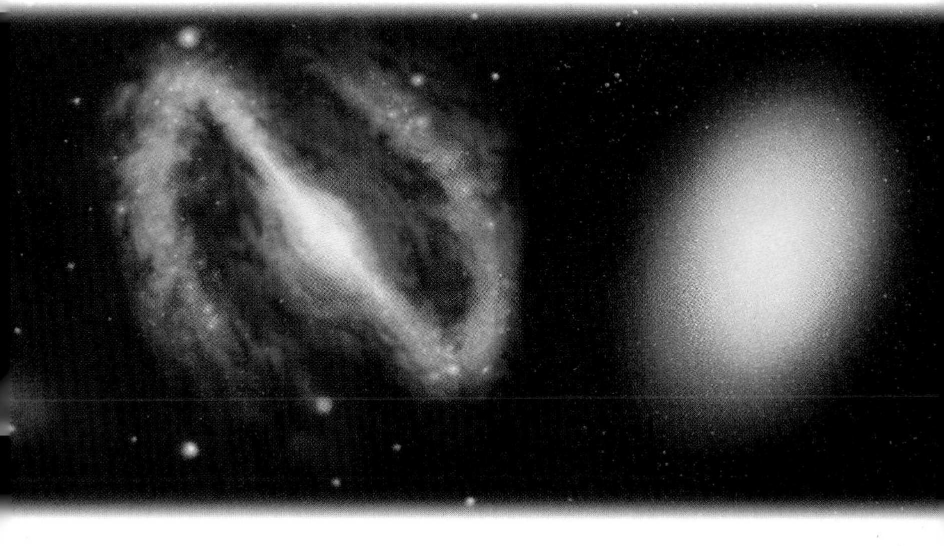

The Milky Way

Our Position in the Milky Way

The Sun is certainly not the center of the universe, or even of the Milky Way. In fact, with its entourage of planets it is located near the edge of the Milky Way, in an area known as the "Sagittarius **arm**."❦ And, just as Earth and the other planets revolve around the Sun, the entire solar system revolves around the center of the Milky Way. The rotation takes 250 million years.

❦ *Arm*

In a galaxy, most stars are found in clusters that are distributed along long curving structures called arms.

Thousands of Stars

When Galileo focused the first telescope on the Milky Way, he discovered thousands of stars. They were not bright enough to be visible to the naked eye, but their accumulation created the white tail that we see. This resembles little dots which, when seen from afar, form the pictures we see on posters.

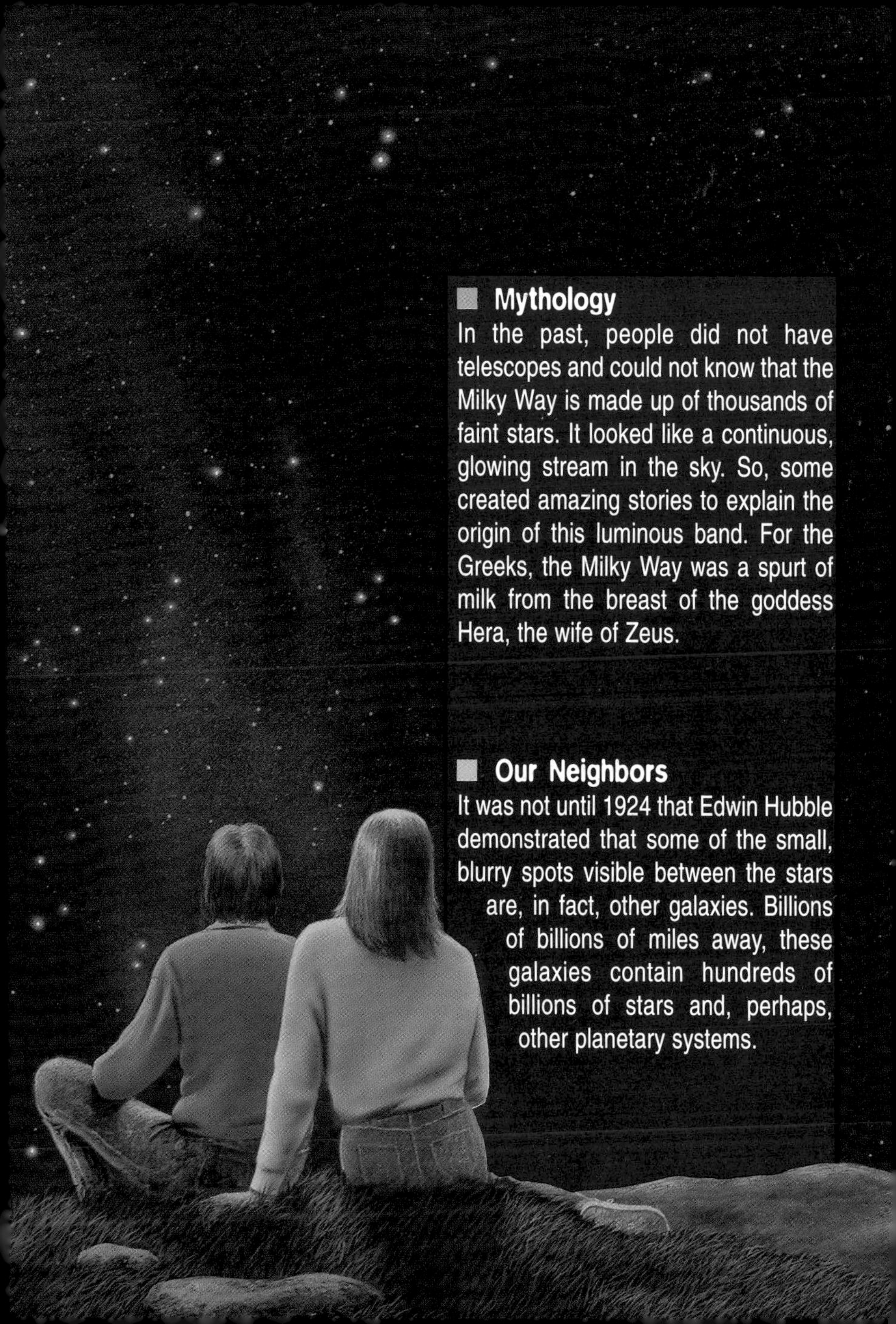

Mythology

In the past, people did not have telescopes and could not know that the Milky Way is made up of thousands of faint stars. It looked like a continuous, glowing stream in the sky. So, some created amazing stories to explain the origin of this luminous band. For the Greeks, the Milky Way was a spurt of milk from the breast of the goddess Hera, the wife of Zeus.

Our Neighbors

It was not until 1924 that Edwin Hubble demonstrated that some of the small, blurry spots visible between the stars are, in fact, other galaxies. Billions of billions of miles away, these galaxies contain hundreds of billions of stars and, perhaps, other planetary systems.

A Starry Sky

To orient themselves easily in the celestial vault, astronomers from ancient times invented figures, constellations, that connect the most brilliant stars.

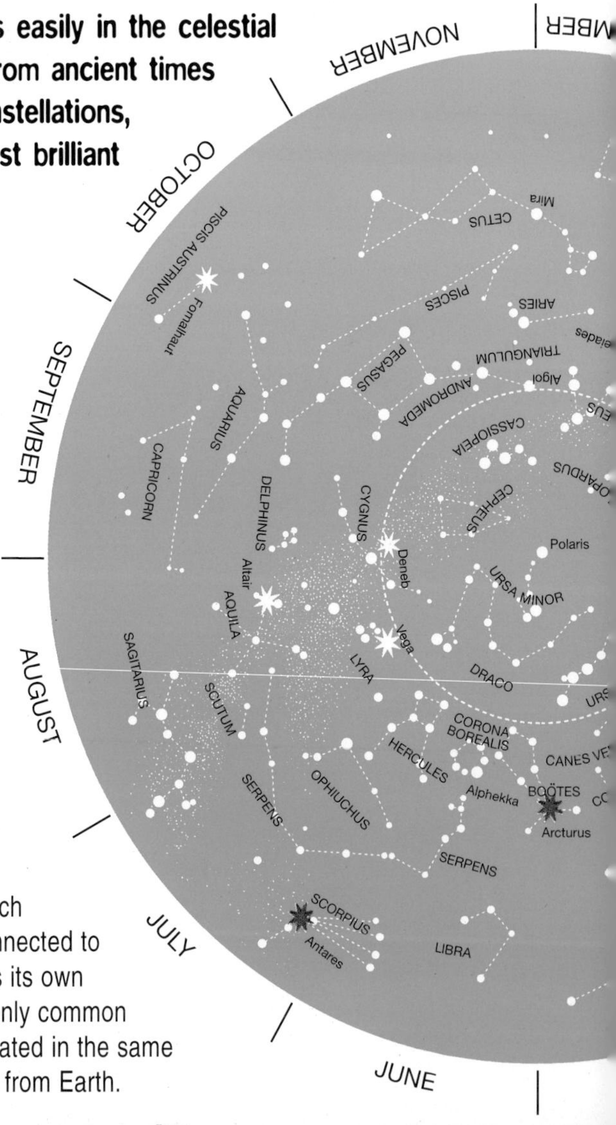

Map of the sky in the Northern Hemisphere

The Stars in the Constellations

In reality, the stars in each constellation are not connected to each other. Each follows its own trajectory. In fact, their only common point is that they are located in the same area of the sky, as seen from Earth.

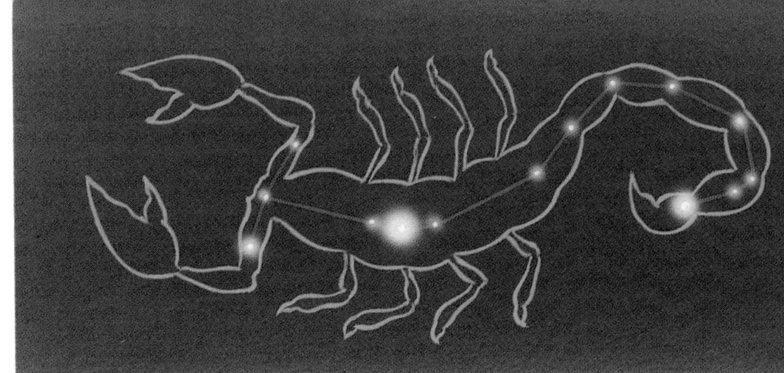

Scorpio constellation

Eighty-eight Constellations

In total, stars visible to the naked eye from around Earth are divided into 88 constellations. This number was established in 1930 by the International Astronomical Union, responsible for problems common to astronomers throughout the world.

Thousands of Stars

In observing the sky with the naked eye (without using binoculars or telescopes) from the countryside or the mountains, it is possible to admire several thousand more or less brilliant stars. In a very dark sky, it is possible to count almost 9,000 stars visible to the naked eye!

Light Pollution

Today, astronomers are disturbed by the expansion of cities. The bigger they are, the more lights are needed to keep them lit. As a result, instead of seeing thousands of stars, a mere 100 are visible.

Activity

Make Your Own

For thousands of years, men have used the stars to tell time. They invented instruments to use. The most well-known celestial clock is the "nocturlabe."

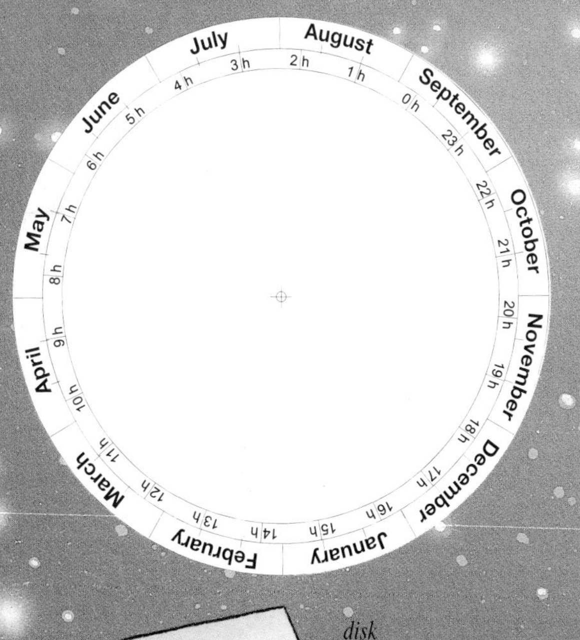

Make Your Own Nocturlabe

You will need:

- 2 pieces of construction pap[er] or cardboard
- a paper fastener
- a pencil
- double-faced tape
- a pair of scissors
- a watch

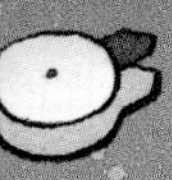

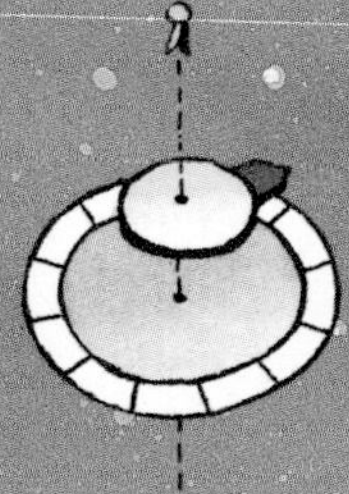

1. Reproduce the disk from the above illustration. From the page of stickers at the back, detach the nocturlabe pointer.

2. Attach the pointer to cardboard.

3. Put the disk and the pointer together with the paper fastener. Attach the nocturlabe to your watch with the double-faced tape.

Activity

Celestial Watch

Use Your Nocturlabe

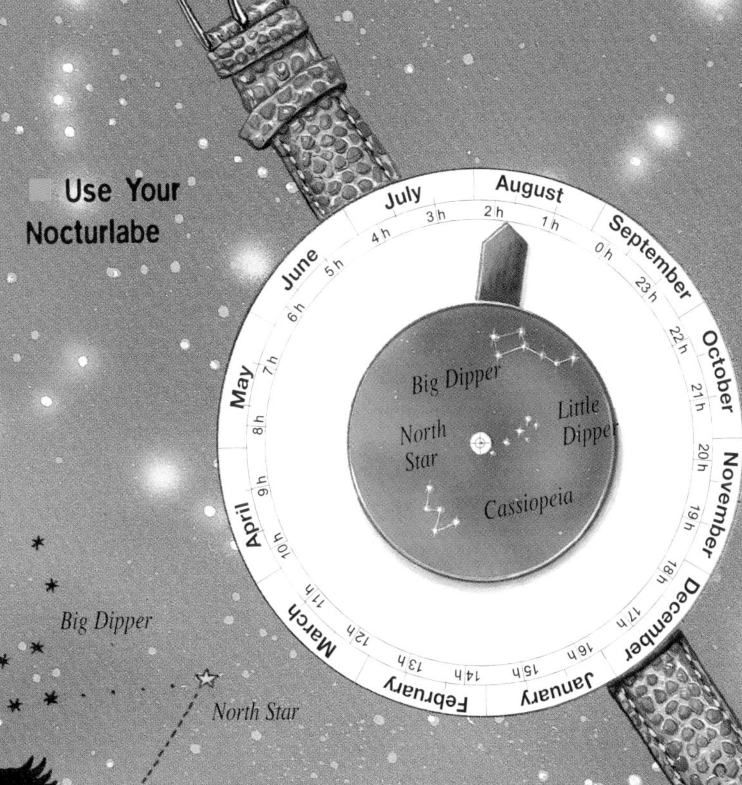

4. On a clear night, find a dark spot, and face toward the north. Find the Big Dipper and the North Star.

5. Face the month of the year toward you. Turn the pointer. The position of the Big Dipper and the North Star on the slide should correspond to what you see in the sky.

6. Read the hour in universal time, indicated by the pointer. Subtract five to eight hours to obtain the actual time in the contiguous United States.

The World of Nebulae

Between the stars there are nebulae, large clouds of gas and dust. They are so large that they could contain Earth or even the entire solar system hundreds of thousands of times over.

Interstellar
Describes the void between the stars, just as "interplanetary" describes the void between the planets.

The Cradle of the Stars

Lost in **interstellar** space, some nebulae contain material created when the universe was born and from the explosion of old stars. Under some conditions, nebulae collapse and form stars and planets.

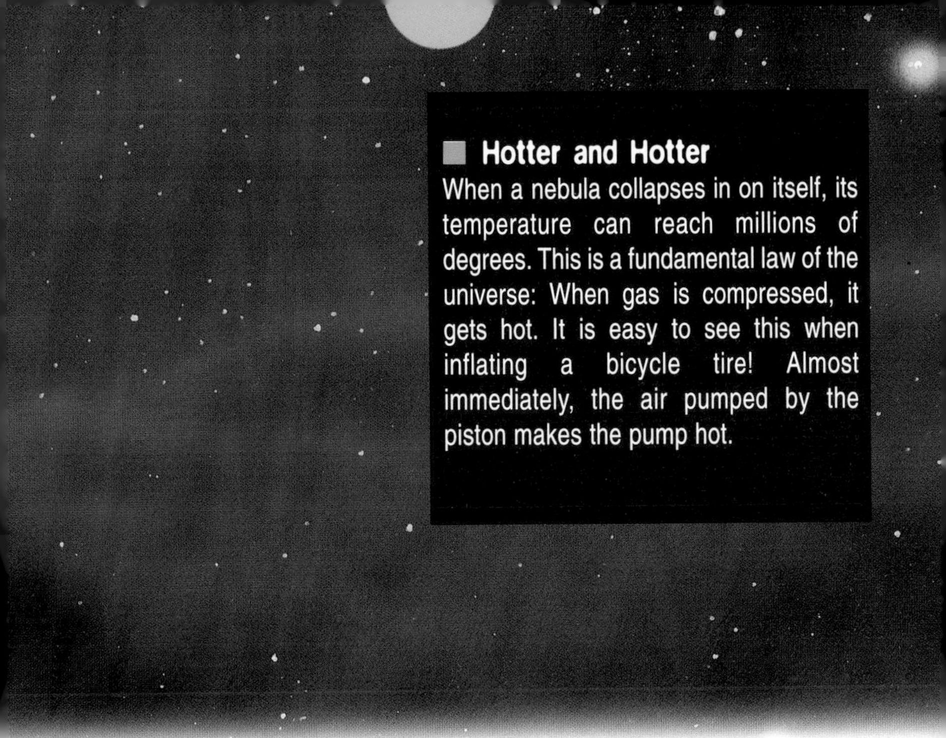

Hotter and Hotter

When a nebula collapses in on itself, its temperature can reach millions of degrees. This is a fundamental law of the universe: When gas is compressed, it gets hot. It is easy to see this when inflating a bicycle tire! Almost immediately, the air pumped by the piston makes the pump hot.

The Horsehead nebula in the constellation Orion.

Stellar Supermarket

You can find everything in nebulae! All the matter that forms the Sun, the Earth, the Moon, and the other bodies in the solar system come from a nebula that collapsed approximately 4.5 billion years ago. Human beings are also made up of these elements, which were created at the birth of the universe and in the stars.

The Collapse of a Nebula

One of the causes of the collapse of a nebula is the explosion of a nearby star. In fact, during the explosion of a star—called a supernova—its matter is projected in all directions with great violence. If it encounters a nebula in its path, it brutally starts the collapse.

The Life of a Star

A Veritable Nuclear Power Plant

Stars are enormous balls of very hot gas. Astronomers estimate the external temperature of the Sun at approximately 6,000°C (10,500°F), much hotter than the flame of a blowtorch. This is already high, but inside a star it is even hotter. At the center of the Sun, the temperature is more than 15 million degrees centigrade (27 million degrees Fahrenheit).

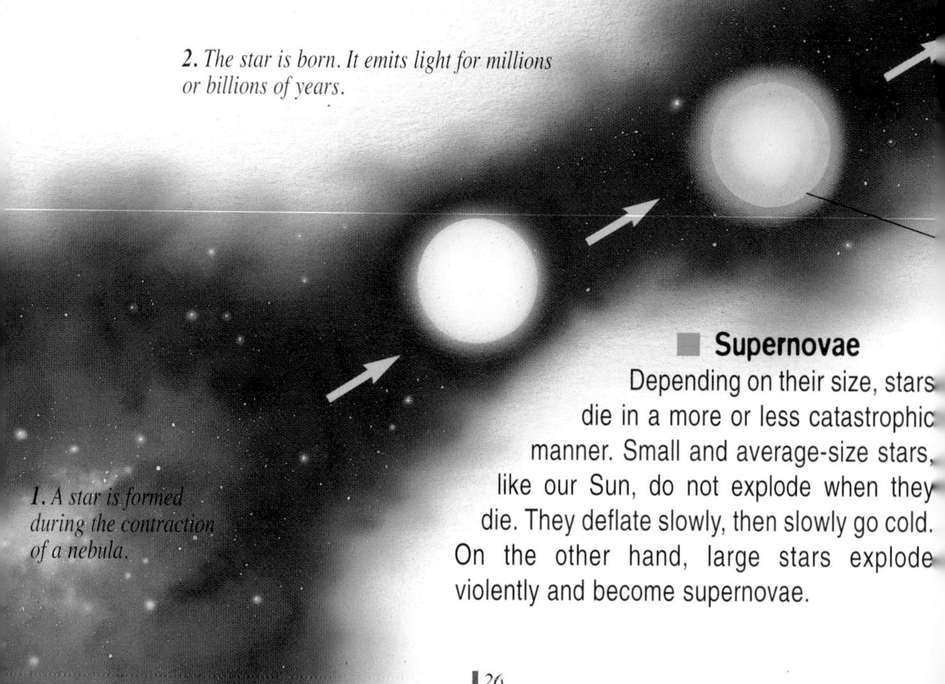

2. The star is born. It emits light for millions or billions of years.

1. A star is formed during the contraction of a nebula.

Supernovae

Depending on their size, stars die in a more or less catastrophic manner. Small and average-size stars, like our Sun, do not explode when they die. They deflate slowly, then slowly go cold. On the other hand, large stars explode violently and become supernovae.

4. The external layers of the star thin out in space.

5. A white dwarf remains, which slowly becomes cold.

3. At the end of its life, the star inflates. Its surface becomes redder and redder.

The Biggest Ones Die Quickly

The largest stars are those that most quickly lose their resources. Thus, astronomers calculate that stars the size of the Sun can live approximately 10 billion years. Our Sun is at the half-point of its life. The largest stars have a life-span of some tens of millions of years, or almost 1,000 times shorter.

Everything Comes from the Stars

Stars are likc factories. In their super-heated centers, they are capable of manufacturing almost all the **elements** contained in the universe—the building blocks of all matter. Those that do not do so in life do so brutally when they explode.

Elements
Oxygen, nitrogen, hydrogen, iron, copper, and lead are elements.

Black Holes

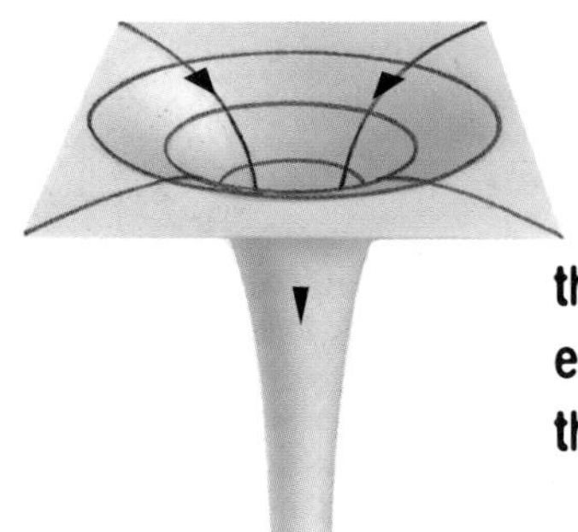

Diagram of a black hole.

Black holes are areas of space so dense that nothing, neither matter nor light, can escape from them...which makes studying them very difficult!

The Origin of Black Holes

In the late eighteenth century, the French astronomer Pierre Simon Laplace had imagined that there could exist, somewhere in the universe, stars that were so dense that nothing could escape from them. He was the first to describe the principle of the black hole.

A black hole in the process of absorbing a star passing nearby.

What is a Black Hole?

To send a rocket into space, it must be propelled at a speed of 7 miles (11.2 km) per second, a speed at which it is free from gravity. On a planet that is more massive than our own, Jupiter for example, a speed of 37.2 miles (60 km) per second would be required. The speed that would be needed to escape from a black hole is greater than that of the speed of light, or 186,282 miles (299,282 km) per second. Thus, no object, not even light can leave this star, which is totally dark!

How Can You See a Black Hole?

The presence of a black hole can only be discovered by observing its action on its environment. In fact, if a star passes nearby, it can be absorbed. Astronomers can then detect the energetic radiation (X rays and gamma rays) that it emits as it progressively disappears into the black hole.

Where Are the Black Holes?

Anywhere that a large star has exploded, it is possible to have a black hole. The most serious "black hole" candidates are found at the center of galaxies. It is there that stars are the closest to each other and that the forces that can make them fall into each other are the greatest.

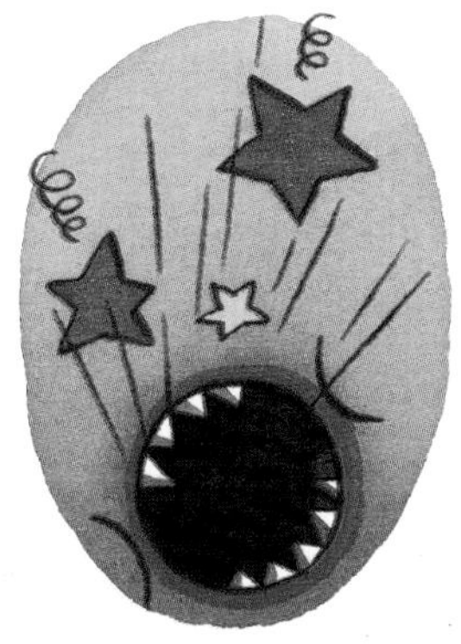

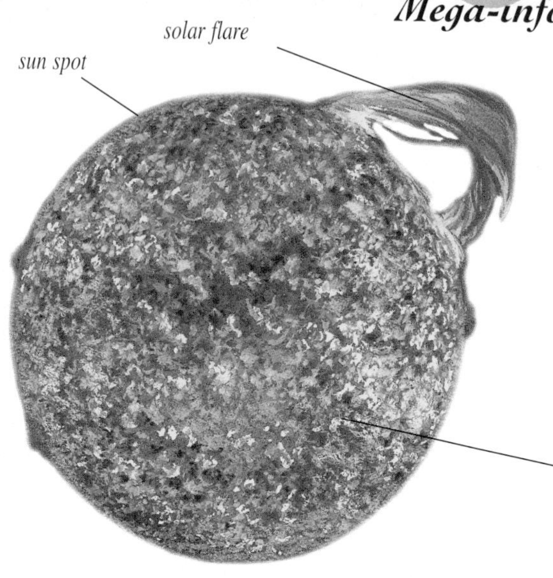

The Sun

Without the Sun, life would be impossible on Earth. It is the Sun that produces the light and heat that are indispensable to us.

The Star that is Closest to Us

If someone someday asks you what star is closest to Earth, do not hesitate for one second to answer "The Sun." The Sun is a gigantic ball of **incandescent** gas with a diameter of 864,000 miles (1.4 million km), or more than three times the distance between Earth and the Moon (238,857 mi., or 384,402 km).

Incandescent
So hot it glows. The Sun shines because of the enormous heat that it releases.

Not Too Hot, Not Too Cold

Our planet appears to have had the good luck to be located at just the right distance from the Sun. Too close, and it would have been too hot and life would not have been able to develop. Too far, and the cold would have prevented the appearance of life. Life on Earth is thus dependent on the warmth that is provided by the Sun. A minor variation in temperature would be enough to turn continents into glaciers or into deserts.

The Future of the Sun

The Sun should continue to shine on Earth for another 5 billion years. Then, times will become very hard for our small planet, which will be tremendously disrupted by the death of the Sun. Either it will disappear totally, absorbed by the Sun, whose outer regions will have expanded as far as the orbit of the planet Venus, or, billions of years later when the Sun shrinks, its atmosphere will have frozen.

The Solar System

Formed from the dust and gas present in the nebula that gave birth to the Sun, the planets orbit around it.

Jupiter

Sun

Earth

Mercury

Mars

Venus

Average distance from the Sun in millions of miles (millions of km).

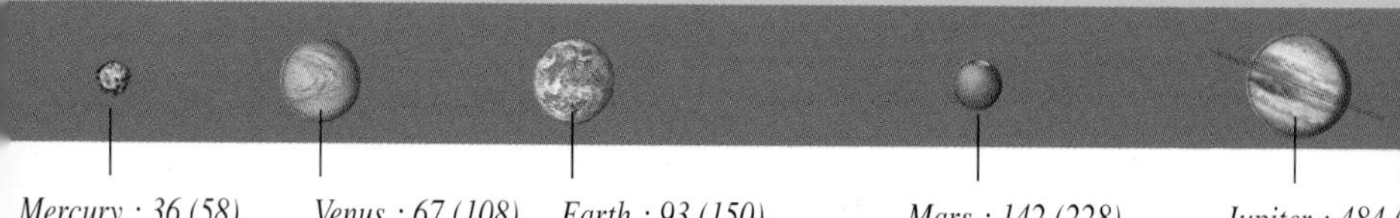

Mercury : 36 (58) *Venus : 67 (108)* *Earth : 93 (150)* *Mars : 142 (228)* *Jupiter : 484 (*

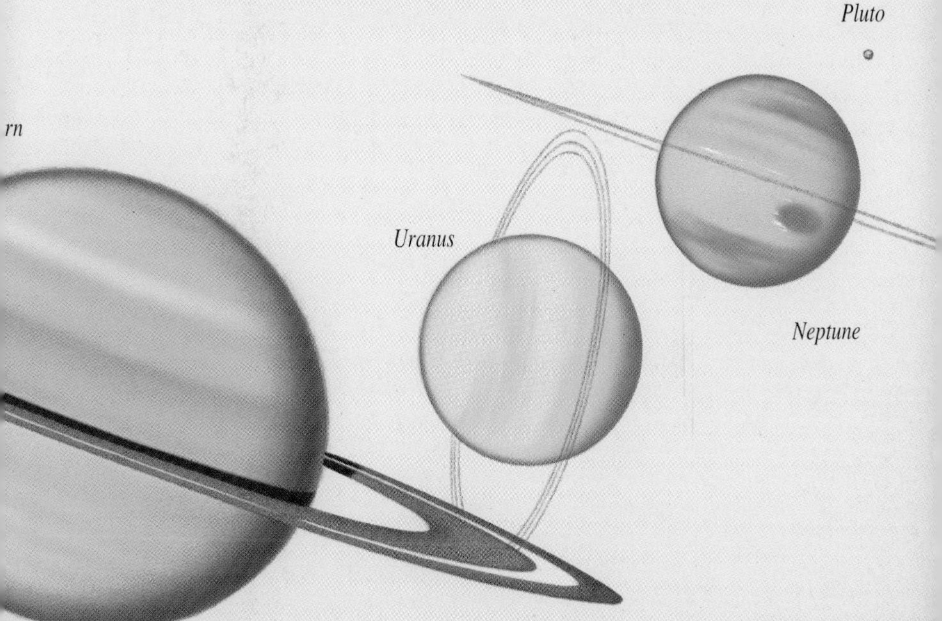

The Creation of Planets

About 4.5 billion years ago, the Sun, the planets, the Moon, comets, and all the objects of the solar system were formed from the same nebula. Naturally, most of the matter from this enormous nebula was taken by the Sun, but enough remained to give birth to the planets that we know today.

Saturn : 888 (1,428) *Uranus : 1,765 (2,872)* *Neptune : 2,791 (4,498)* *Pluto : 3,64 (5,910)*

Amazing

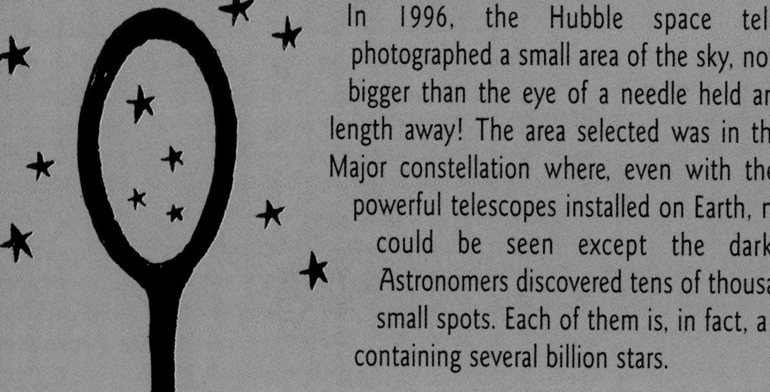

50,000 GALAXIES IN THE EYE OF A NEEDLE...

In 1996, the Hubble space telescope photographed a small area of the sky, not much bigger than the eye of a needle held an arm's length away! The area selected was in the Ursa Major constellation where, even with the most powerful telescopes installed on Earth, nothing could be seen except the dark sky! Astronomers discovered tens of thousands of small spots. Each of them is, in fact, a galaxy containing several billion stars.

THE EARTH IS SLOWING DOWN

About 3 billion years ago, Earth revolved much faster. Instead of 24 hours, a day was only 18 or 19 hours long! But the Moon has been slowly receding from us, resulting in the steady slowing down of Earth's rotation. Astronomers have calculated that, in a few hundred million years, one day will last more than 25 hours.

but True!

BILLIONS OF PLANETS?

Giant planets are in orbit around some of the stars that are the closest to us. The formation of planetary systems like the solar system appears to be a normal phenomenon in the universe. If astronomers have not yet detected planets the size of Earth, it is only because their instruments are not sufficiently powerful!

THE BOMBARDMENT CONTINUES!

Earth has been subject to violent bombardments of meteorites since its formation. But clouds, wind, rain, vegetation, and volcanoes quickly erase their traces. Less powerful than before, the bombardment of meteorites continues. On average, 60,000 tons of meteorites fall on Earth each year, mainly in the form of microscopic dust but also as stones that fall in the oceans and the deserts and sometimes in cities.

The Planets

There are a total of nine planets. Those closest to the Sun are small and dense. Those furthest from the Sun are voluminous and not very dense.

Name: **Mercury**
Diameter: 3,031 miles (4,878 km)
Temperature: 800°F (400°C),day, –300°F (–170°C), night
Length of revolution: 88 earth days
Special characteristics: one of the smallest planets in the solar system; a ball of desert rock; no atmosphere.

Name: **Venus**
Diameter: 7,521 miles (12,104 km)
Temperature: about 900°F (474°C), day and night
Length of revolution: 225 earth days
Special characteristics: has tens of thousands of volcanoes, but they appear to be extinct.

Name: **Earth**
Diameter: 7,926 miles (12,756 km)
Temperature: approximately 57°F (14°C), day and night
Length of revolution: 365.25 earth days
Special characteristics: has an atmosphere; the temperature there supports life.

Name: **Mars**
Diameter: 4,223 miles (6,796 km)
Temperature: –24°F (–31°C), day, –148°F (–100°C), night
Length of revolution: 687 earth days
Special characteristics: desert of sand, volcanic ash, and ice without any form of life.

Name: **Jupiter**
Diameter: 88,846 miles (142,984 km)
Temperature: –250°F (–157°C)
Length of revolution: 4,332 earth days
Special characteristics: a tremendously thick atmosphere, it may have a solid core the size of a dozen Earths; very fine rings; sixteen **moons** that revolve around it.

Moon
Natural satellite of a planet; can refer specifically to Earth's satellite.

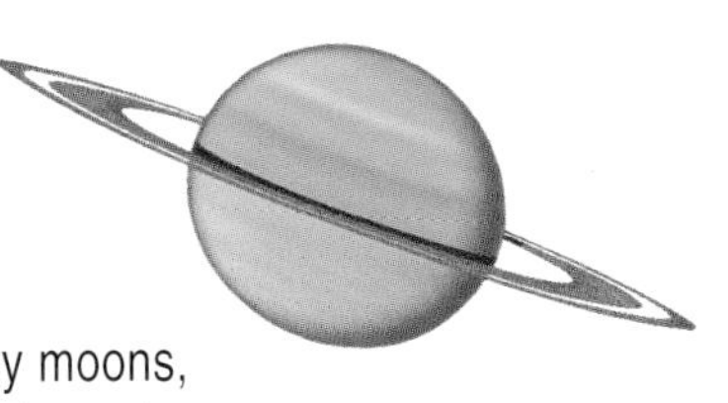

Name: **Saturn**
Diameter: 74,898 miles (120,536 km)
Temperature: –288°F (–178°C)
Length of revolution: 10,759 earth days
Special characteristics: accompanied by twenty moons, the largest of which, Titan, possesses a thick atmosphere.

Name: **Uranus**
Diameter: 31,763 miles (51,118 km)
Temperature: –357°F (–216°C)
Length of revolution: 30,688 earth days
Special characteristics: observed by Voyager 2 in January 1986; one of its moons, Miranda, has a cliff 12.4 miles (20 km) high; a thick atmosphere.

Name: **Neptune**
Diameter: 30,800 miles (49,500 km)
Temperature: –353°F (–214°C)
Length of revolution: 60,181 earth days
Special characteristics: flown over by Voyager 2 in August 1989; possesses a thick atmosphere of hydrogen and helium.

Name: **Pluto**
Diameter: 1,430 miles (2,300 km)
Temperature: –374.8°F (–226°C)
Length of revolution: 90,470 earth days
Special characteristics: the smallest planet in the solar system; the Sun is so far away from it that it is only a bright star in an eternal black sky; has one moon, Charon.

Earth and the Moon

The pair formed by Earth and the Moon is exceptional in the solar system. Other planets have moons, but the dimensions of Earth and its satellite make it instead a "twin planet."

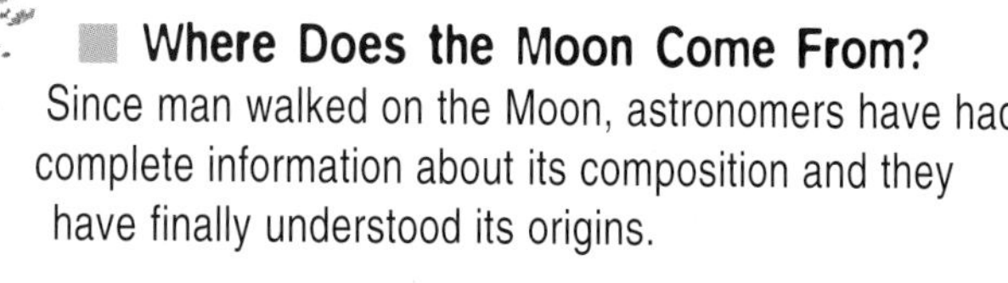

Where Does the Moon Come From?

Since man walked on the Moon, astronomers have had complete information about its composition and they have finally understood its origins.

1. Earth, still young, collides with a planet two times smaller than itself. One part of this planet merges with Earth.

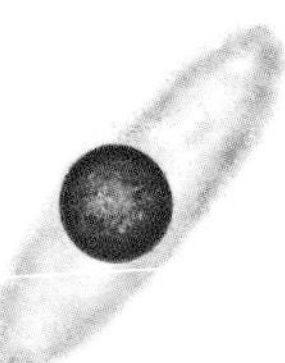

2. The violent shock projects enormous quantities of rocks and dust into space.

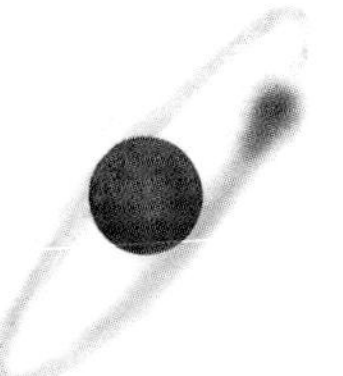

3. They come together to give birth to the Moon.

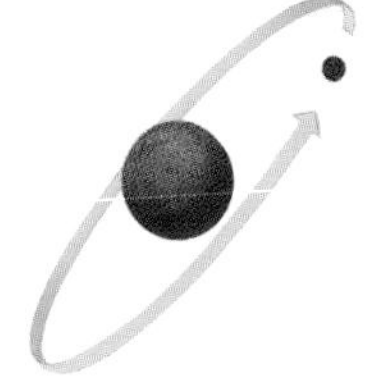

4. The Moon revolves around Earth.

A Rare Couple

Only two planets possess a natural satellite of a size comparable to their own: Earth and Pluto. The moon of Pluto is called Charon and is only half the size of its planet. As for our Moon, its diameter is 2,160 miles (3,476 km), slightly larger than one quarter of Earth's diameter.

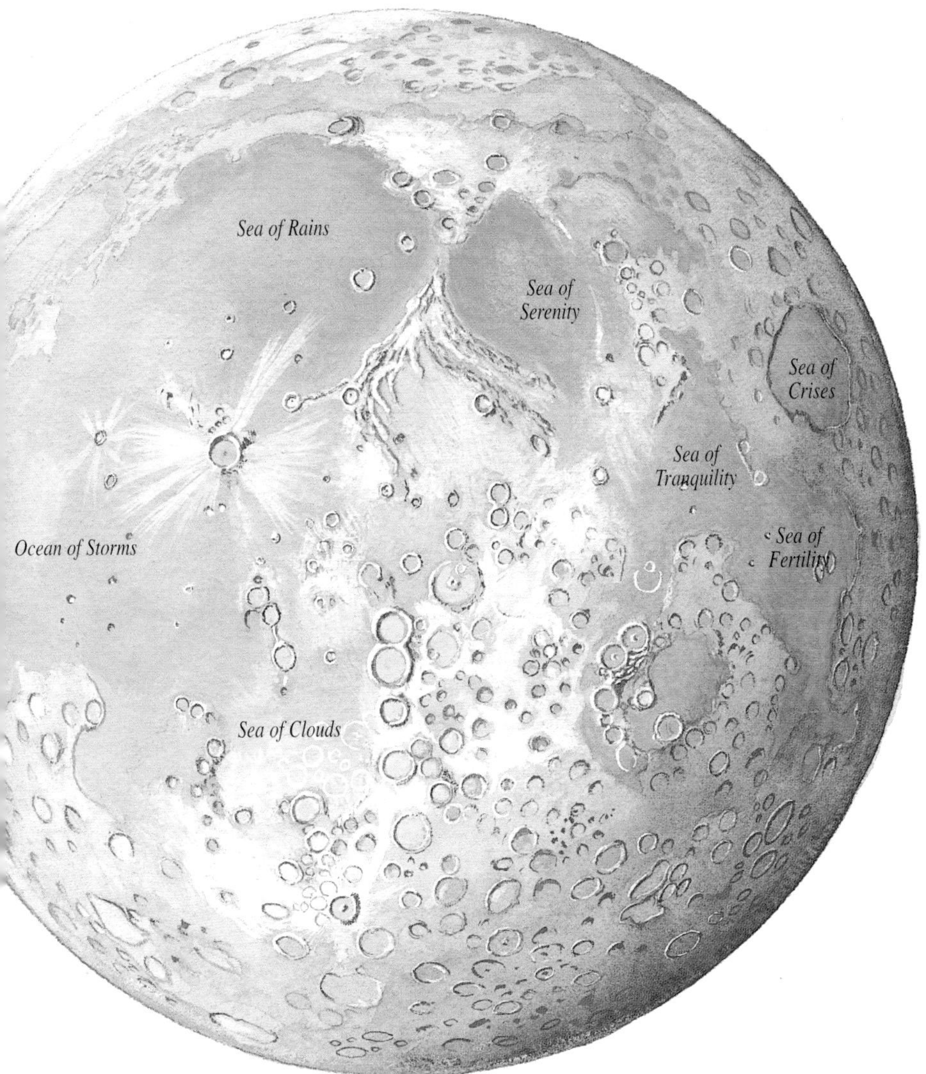

The Tides

The influence of the Moon is felt through tides. The combined influence of the Moon and the Sun moves the oceans, which cover 75 percent of our globe. There are also “solid tides,” which appear as deformations in Earth’s crust.

The Moon always shows us the same face.

Comets

■ Dirty Snowballs

When the solar system was formed, 4.5 billion years ago, the dust and gas that was not entirely incorporated into the Sun and planets formed large balls of dusty snow—comets. When these icy blocks get close to the Sun, they partially vaporize. They create an envelope of gas and dust, which may stretch out to form a long tail, sometimes visible to the naked eye.

The Original Solar System

There exists a large "reservoir" of comets beyond the orbit of Uranus and Neptune. These are areas of the solar system so far away from the Sun that its rays are not capable of melting icy bodies. The nuclei of these comets have remained practically unchanged since their creation and they are capable, therefore, of serving as a source of very precise information about the era in which the planets were formed.

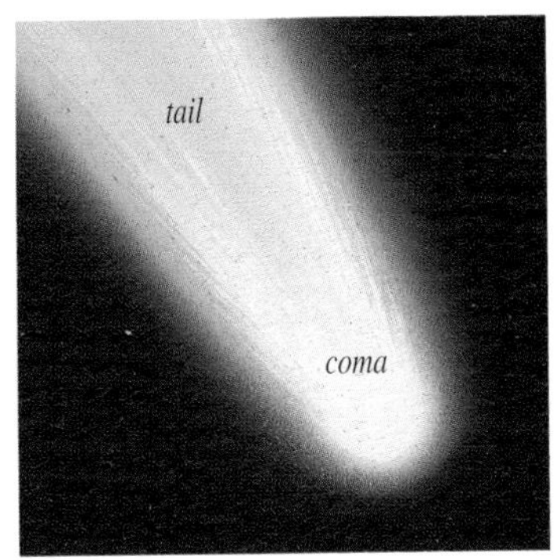

How Does it Work?

For astronomers to be able to study a comet, it must leave its far-off reservoir and come close to the Sun. The closer it gets, the more the temperature increases on its surface. Upon reaching approximately 621 million miles (a billion km) from our star, the ice in the comet's nucleus begins to vaporize. Thus, with each passage close to the Sun, a comet loses some of its matter!

The Celebrities

The most famous of the thousands of comets observed in thousands of years are without a doubt Halley's Comet and Hale-Bopp. Halley's Comet passes close to the Sun and Earth every 76 years. Hale-Bopp was easily visible to the naked eye throughout the Northern Hemisphere in the spring of 1997 and in the Southern Hemisphere at the beginning of the summer of 1997.

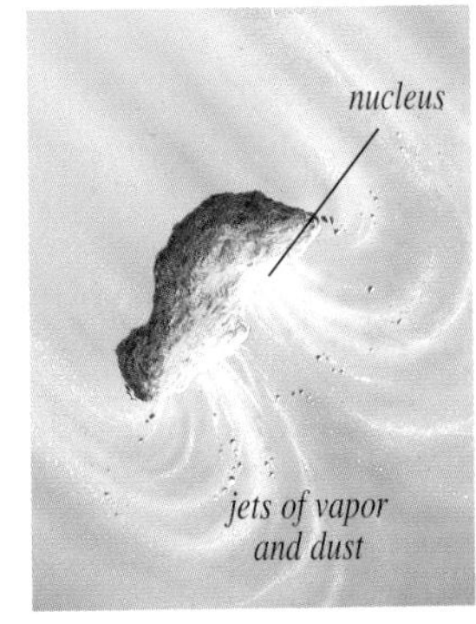

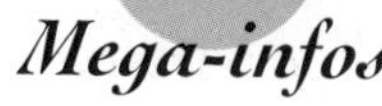

Shooting Stars

In steadily observing the sky for several minutes at night, it is not unusual to see shooting stars.

Shooting Stars

Each year, at almost the same time, Earth encounters dust in the course of its annual rotation around the Sun. In rubbing against the gas of the atmosphere, the dust becomes hot and ends up bursting into flames. Seen from Earth, these small moving flames form shooting stars. They occur in groups, such as the Perseids.

Shooting stars and asteroids are debris from the formation of the solar system that circulates between the planets.

Where Do Shooting Stars Come From?

The dust particles that give birth to shooting stars are debris that has drifted among the planets since the solar system was formed or that was left by comets. The smallest, the size of a grain of sand, hardly weigh more than a few tenths of a gram. The largest can weigh up to several dozen grams and resemble bits of gravel.

and Meteorites

Small Particles of Dust and Large Stones

When the dust particles colliding with our planet are larger than average, they burn much more slowly and it is possible to see what are called "meteors." A celestial meteor can become as bright as the full moon for several seconds and leave a long incandescent trail behind it.

Meteorites

Several times a year, Earth encounters even larger stones, weighing several pounds or more. They slow their flight through the atmosphere before any significant amount melts. When they land, they do very little harm, often partially burying themselves in the ground. They can measure from a few inches to a yard or two. Rarely, a meteorite can form a huge crater, such as the Meteor Crater of Arizona—4,150 feet (1,265 m) wide and 570 feet (174 m) deep.

Activity

Collect Shooting Star

Each year, more than 60,000 tons of dust from shooting stars falls on Earth. Nothing is easier than collecting some of this matter after a beautiful night of shooting stars.

Advice
Wait for the first rainy day after a shower of shooting stars!

Activity

You will need:
- a basin
- a magnet
- a spoon and a knife
- a sheet of tissue paper (optional)
- a magnifying glass

1. Collect enough rainwater to just cover the bottom of a basin. Put it in a warm, airy place so that the water can evaporate.

2. When all of the water has disappeared, carefully scrape the bottom of the basin with the knife to collect a bit of dust. Gently crush it with the back of the spoon.

3. Wrap the magnet in a sheet of tissue paper and pass it over the dust particles. The small fragments will be attracted because dust particles from shooting stars often contain iron. Under the magnifying glass, they appear black and do not have jagged edges because they melted while traveling through the atmosphere.

Ground Observation

Since the seventeenth century, astronomers have invented instruments to observe the skies. These range from simple binoculars to professional telescopes, larger than buildings.

Eyes to See

Nature has given humans very capable eyes. During the day, they enable us to see near or far, in relief and in color. In the darkness, things are slightly different as we do not use our eyes in the same way as in full daylight. Our night vision is not sensitive to colors but we are able to distinguish the tiny glow of the stars.

The Invention of Lenses and Telescopes

Until 1609, astronomers observed the skies only with the naked eye. Galileo was the first to use a telescope to look at the stars. After that, a number of other instruments were invented, such as Newton's telescope (invented by the great English physicist Isaac Newton). These instruments are still used by amateur astronomers.

The European VLT, comprising four of the largest telescopes in the world, is located in Chile.

The Biggest Instruments in the World

Seventeen, or even thirty-five feet (five, ten meters) in diameter, the mirrors of telescopes are larger and larger. Today, telescopes larger than even thirty-five feet are being built. They are all installed on high mountains to take advantage of a perfectly transparent sky throughout the year. They are found on the island of Hawaii, on the tops of the Andes Cordillera in South America, in Australia, and at other sites.

Telescopes of the Future

It is too expensive to send large telescopes into space, so astronomers in recent years have begun to construct giant instruments. They will be installed in the best astronomical sites on the planet. Equipped with devices that correct for atmospheric **turbulence**, they will make it possible to obtain pictures as precise as those taken in space.

Turbulence
Whirlwinds in the air that are responsible for making the stars twinkle.

Observation

Observing the sky from Earth is practical, but clouds always appear at the worst possible time and interfere with the admiration of the stars...

■ The Disappearance of the Atmosphere

The major problem for observers of the skies is the atmosphere. It moves all the time under the action of the wind and it is frequently visited by undesirable clouds. One way to eliminate the problems caused by the atmosphere and its turbulence is to install telescopes in space.

■ The Hubble Space Telescope

Hubble is the largest of the telescopes in orbit around our planet. It was put into orbit on April 25, 1990, by the American space shuttle *Discovery,* at an altitude of more than 370 miles (600 km). Since then, astronauts have visited it twice: first in December 1993 to make repairs, then in February 1997 to install new receivers. Both of these efforts greatly improved its performance.

in Space

The diameter of the primary mirror is 8 feet (2.4 m). Hubble is as big as a double-decker bus.

■ Specialized Telescopes

Even though it is spoken about a great deal, the Hubble space telescope is not the only one in orbit around Earth. There are several astronomical observation satellites that have examined the universe for the past several years. These instruments are sensitive to ultraviolet, infrared, gamma, or X rays. Many rays reach the surface of our planet only partially, or not at all, because they are stopped by the atmosphere.

An Astronomer's Job

Many children dream of becoming astronomers. Unfortunately, there are only a few observatories on Earth and positions for professional astronomers are rare.

A Job as Old as the World

Today's astronomer does not at all resemble the scientist of old, who was often shown wearing a large, pointed hat covered with stars. Using the most modern techniques to observe the skies, today's astronomer can remotely control a telescope located thousands of miles away, or orient the Hubble space telescope to take photographs of the planet Mars or the Milky Way.

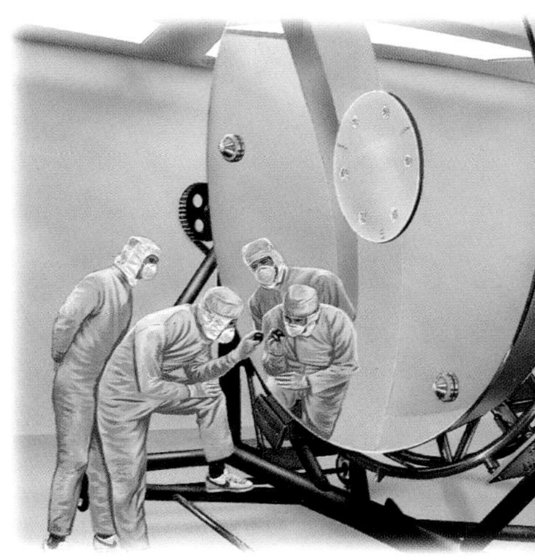

What Does an Astronomer Do?

Some astronomers travel a great deal to observe and photograph the skies with the different telescopes available on Earth. Others work solely in front of their computer screens, studying pictures from space telescopes and automatic probes that visit the different planets of the solar system.

ing a telescope mirror.

How Do You Become an Astronomer?

The position of astronomer in an observatory is obtained only after many years of university study. A scientific or technical degree is required. The future astronomer must have more than ten years of training in physics and in mathematics. This training will be used every day in trying to understand how the universe functions.

How Many Astronomers Are There?

The total number of astronomers is very small: only a few hundred in Europe, three or four thousand in the United States, and a total of seven thousand throughout the world. But astronomers are surrounded by numerous engineers, technicians, and computer scientists who design and manufacture the more and more powerful instruments that make it possible to probe the universe.

Meeting Extraterrestrials. On this green planet, the you count? Answer on page 63.

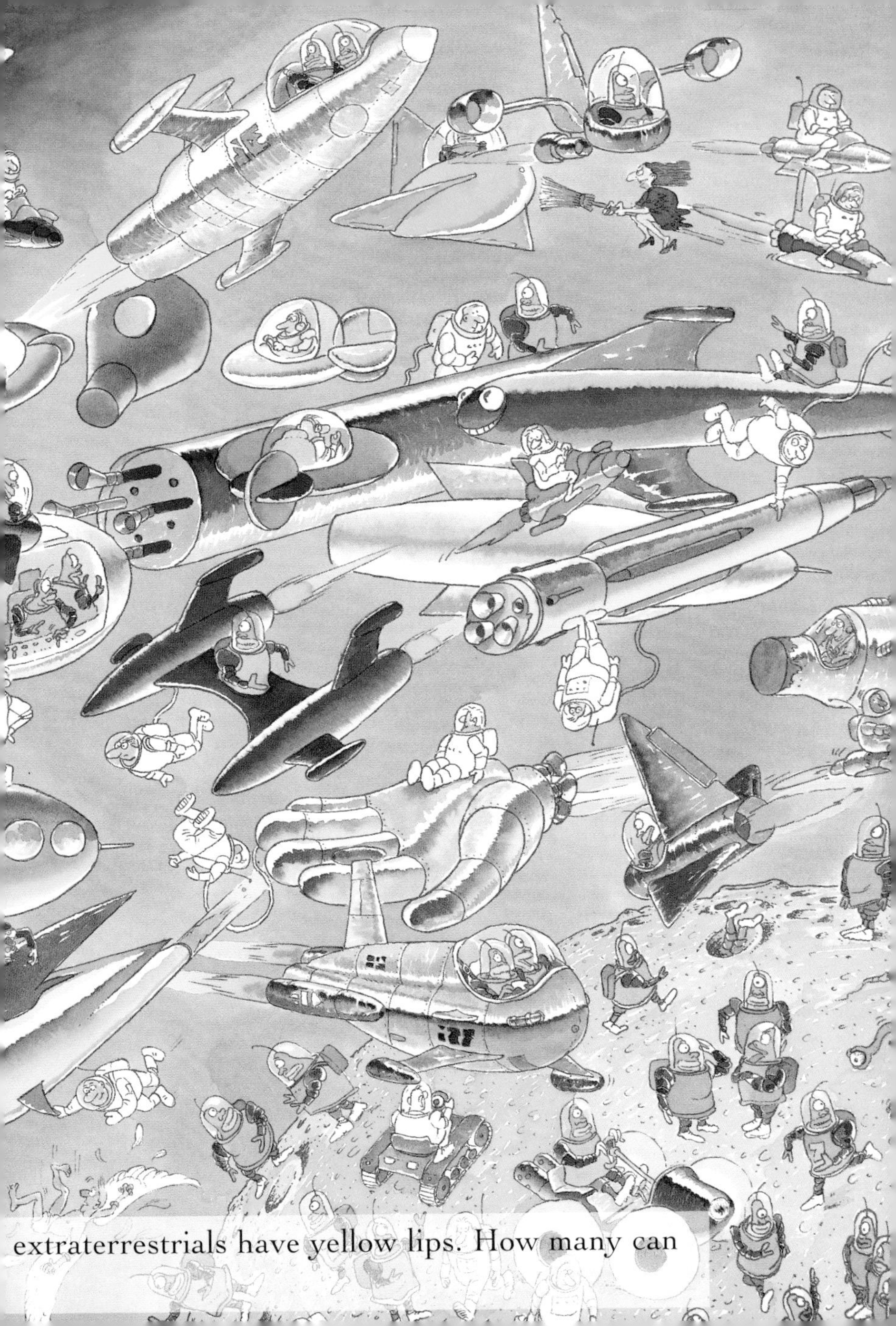

extraterrestrials have yellow lips. How many can

Is There Life

In all the universe, Earth is the only known place where life has appeared. Other planets in the solar system are hopelessly empty, and the stars tell us nothing.

Is There Life Elsewhere in the Universe?

The example of Earth proves that the conditions required for life to appear have occurred at least once in the universe. When we know that there are billions of stars like the Sun in the Milky Way, as well as tens of billions of galaxies, it seems obvious that these conditions must have occurred somewhere else. But how can we know where?

Is There Life Elsewhere in the Solar System?

The exploration of the other planets in the solar system began on August 27,1962, when the American space probe *Mariner 2* was launched. It flew over Venus several months later. We have also sent out interplanetary probes to study other bodies in the solar system. Conclusion: Earth is the only planet that supports life. Even Mars is only a vast desert of volcanic ash and ice.

Elsewhere?

Searching for Extraterrestrials

Persuaded that life exists elsewhere than on Earth, a group of astronomers has for the past several years tried to listen to the universe using enormous radio antennae. In this way they hope one day to receive intelligent signals containing extraterrestrial messages. They are working for a research program called SETI (Search for Extraterrestrial Intelligence).

The Universe, Literature

The sky does not belong only to astronomers. Writers and filmmakers have also been attracted by the beauty of the stars.

[...] it is sweet, through the mists, to see born
The star in the sky, the lamp in the window,
The rivers of coal climb into the firmament
And the moon pours out its pale enchantment. [...]

Charles Baudelaire, "Landscape," *Flowers of Evil,* 1857

Nothing New Under the Stars...

Science fiction books and films like the *Star Wars* series quickly transport us from one planet to another and make us discover a thousand forms of extravagant life. But this is nothing new! Movies did not exist 5,000 years ago, and the hero of the epic *Gilgamesh,* one of the first "books" of humanity, moved easily between strange worlds and met extraordinary creatures, like the terrible scorpion-men who guarded the gates of the kingdom of the dead at the bottom of the Milky Way.

Cover of a 1961 science fiction magazine.

and Science Fiction

[...] In one of the stars I shall be living. In one of them I shall be laughing. And so it will be as if all the stars were laughing, when you look at the sky at night. You—only you—will have stars that can laugh! [...]

The Little Prince, Antoine de Saint-Exupéry,1943

True or

The lights in cities disturb astronomers in their observations.

True.

All of the galaxies in the universe join together to for[m] gigantic pinwheels.

False. It is the stars that join together in this manner in the Milky Way. The galaxies are distributed throughout the universe like dust on empty bubbles.

The Milky Way visible in the sky is in fact our galaxy seen from one direction.

True.

All of the elements that we know on Earth are found in the universe.

rue. As far as astronomers
an see, the elements are the
ame everywhere.

False?

■ **For the Maya, Earth was covered by the shell of a giant tortoise.**

False. For the Maya, Earth was flat and balanced on the back of a giant tortoise.

■ **The Sun is located at the center of the Milky Way.**

False. The Sun is situated most of the way to the edge of the Milky Way.

■ **The largest stars are the first to disappear.**

True. They use up their energy supply more quickly.

■ **The Sun is a planet.**

False. The Sun is a star.

True or

■ **Dinosaurs died out after the fall of an enormous meteorite on Earth.**

True. This meteorite fell 65 million years ago in the Yucatan region of Mexico.

■ **A black hole is a mass so dense that no light can escape it.**

True.

■ **The closest star to Earth is the Sun.**

True.

■ **Galileo invented the telescope.**

False. Galileo was the first to use a telescope to observe the stars, but the instrument was invented decades before in Italy.

False?

The twelve men who have walked on the Moon were all military men.

False. Harrison Schmitt, who was part of the last Apollo mission in 1972, was a civilian, a geologist by training.

The largest telescope in the world is the Hubble space telescope.

False. The Hubble space telescope is the largest telescope in orbit, but on Earth there are telescopes three or four times larger.

The Sun was born at the beginning of the universe.

False. The Sun and the planets of the solar system were formed only 4.5 billion years ago and the universe is more than 10 billion years old.

Shooting stars are small comets.

False. Shooting stars are meteorites, small particles of dust that burn up upon entering the atmosphere. Comets are balls of ice and dust that orbit the Sun.

Index

Solution to game on pages 52–53

You should have found seventeen extraterrestrials with yellow lips.

Photo credits for picture cards (left to right)

Top: J. Schad/Explorer; Bayeux Tapestry – 11th century, with the special permission of the city of Bayeux; Florida Today Liaison Gamma; G.Cozzi/ANA; NASA/Science Photo Library/Cosmos; *Mars Attacks*/Cat's Collection. **Bottom**: *The Empire Strikes Back*/Collection Christophe L.; B.Yen/Gamma; J. Frassanito/NASA/Science Photo Library/Cosmos; Archives Nathan; Science Photo Library/Cosmos; C. Butler/Science Photo Library/Cosmos; **Page 56**: top right *Star Trek*/Cat's Collection; bottom left Archives Nathan; **Page 57**: Excerpt from *The Little Prince* by Antoine de Saint-Exupéry, ©1943, renewed 1971 Harcourt Brace. Reprinted by permission of Harcourt Brace.

Photo credits for stickers

Gamma; P. Hurlin/Explorer; Gamma; *Mars Attacks*/collection Christophe L.; *Invasion of the Saucer Men*/collection Christophe L.; Van Waay/Explorer; J. L. Charmet/Archives de l'Académie des sciences; NASA Liaison/Gamma; D.Ducros/Science Photo Library/Cosmos; Coll.E.S/Explorer; Coll.E.S/Explorer; Archives Nathan/ESA.

Illustrations

Robert Barborini, Eric Doxat, Christophe Drochon, Daniel Guerrier, Olivier Hubert, Martin Matje, Philippe Münch, Delphine Renon, David Sala. Cover: Jean-François Pénichoux

The title of the French edition is *L'espace infini*. Published by Les Editions Nathan, Paris.

All inquiries should be addressed to:
Barron's Educational Series, Inc.
250 Wireless Boulevard
Hauppauge, New York, 11788
http://www.barronseduc.com

Library of Congress Catalog Card No.: 98-74447
International Standard Book No.: 0-7641-5180-0

Printed in Italy 9 8 7 6 5 4 3 2 1

Stickers

Hubble telescope

Astronaut

European probe
Ulysse

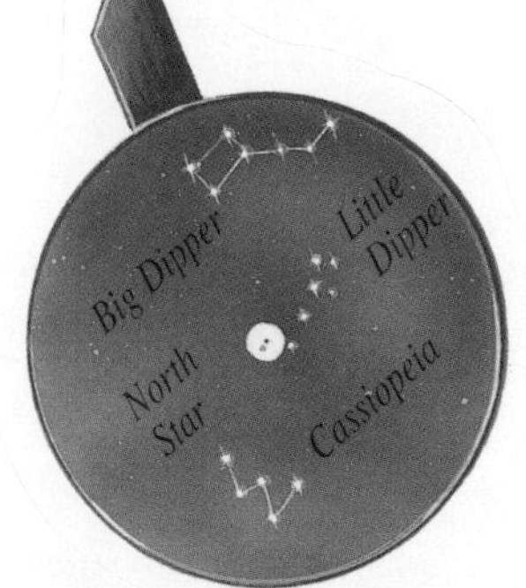

pointer
of nocturlabe
(activity pages 22–23)

Chief of the Martians in
Mars Attacks

Invasion of the Saucer Men

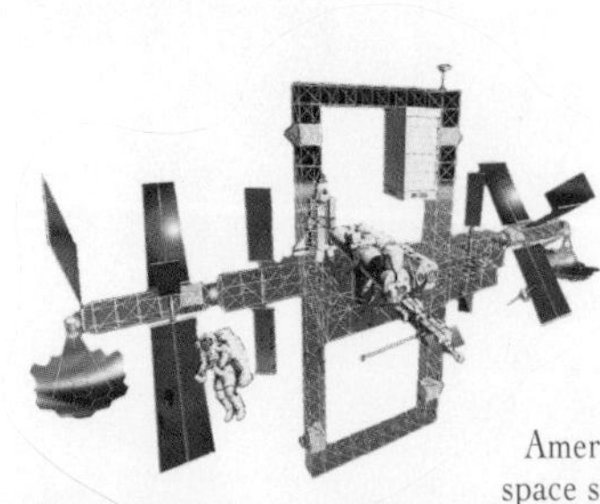

American
space station
Columbus

Stickers

Drawing of flying chariot, 18th century

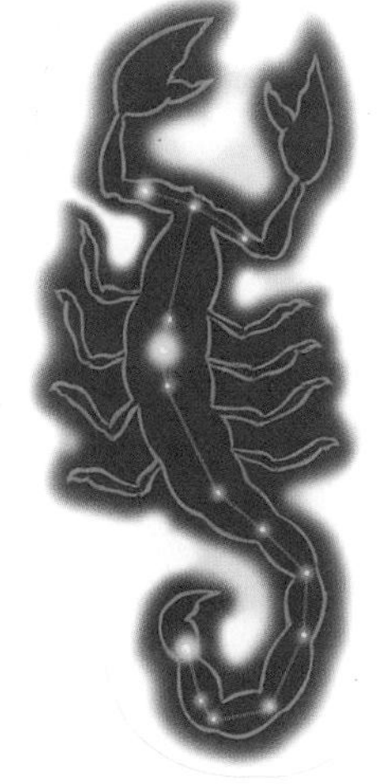

Scorpio Constellation

Ariane 5 at takeoff

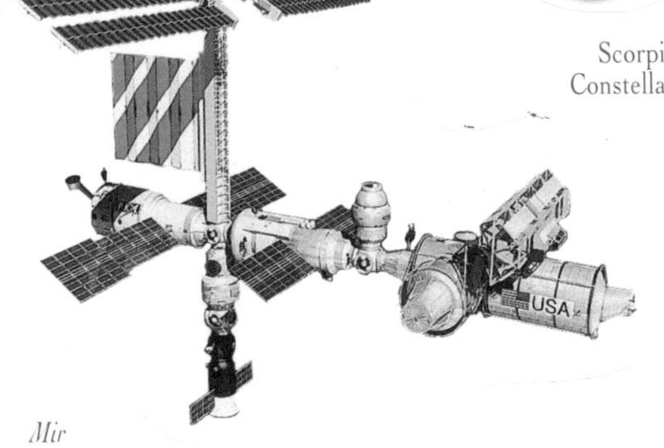

Mir space station

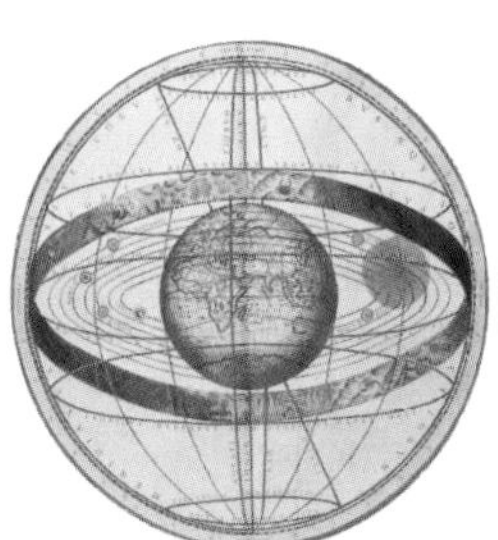

Ptolemy's system, with the Earth at the center, 11th century

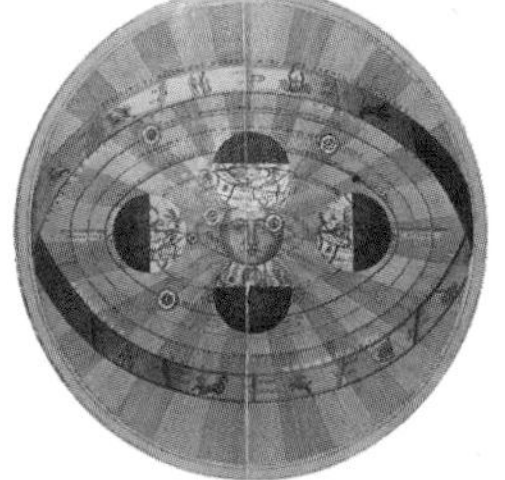

Copernicus' system, with the Sun at the center, 16th century

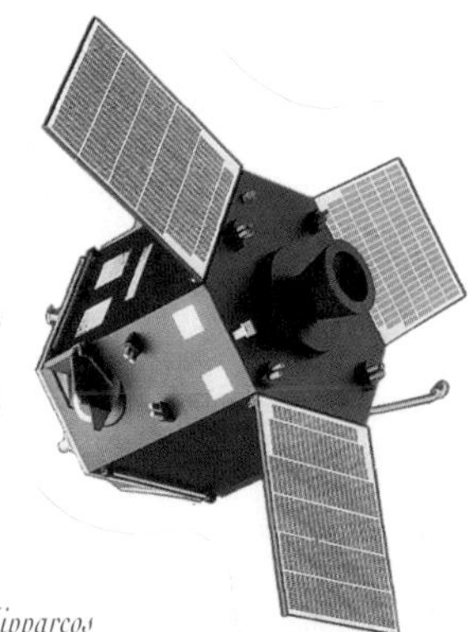

Hipparcos satellite observatory

HAROLD

Titles in the Megascope series:

The Adventures of the Great Explorers
Amazing Nature
Brilliant and Crazy Inventions
Infinite Space
Life in the Middle Ages
Mysteries, True and False
Our Planet Earth
The Pharaohs of Ancient Egypt
Searching for Human Origins
Understanding the Human Body

Barron's Educational Series, Inc.
250 Wireless Boulevard
Hauppauge, NY 11788